20p

CASTLES

This book belongs to:

On the sketch of a castle below there are 15 details. When you next visit a castle try to I-Spy some of them. If you do, you can award yourself points as shown towards your total of 1000.

Arrow loophole	10	Keep	10
Battlements	10	Machicolations	20
Crosslet loophole	20	Moat	20
Curtain wall	10	Motte	15
Drawbridge	15	Outer Bailey	10
Gatehouse	10	Portcullis	20
Inner Bailey	10	Turret	10
Inner Gateway	10		

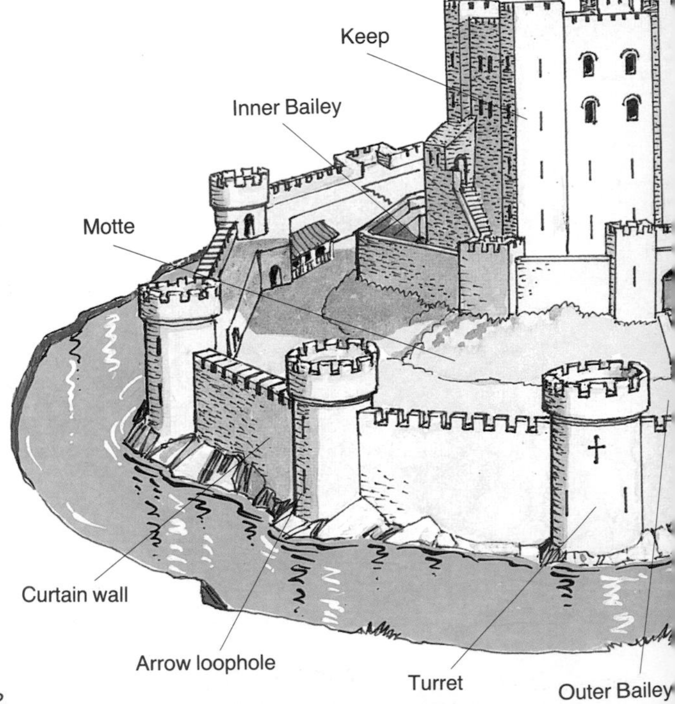

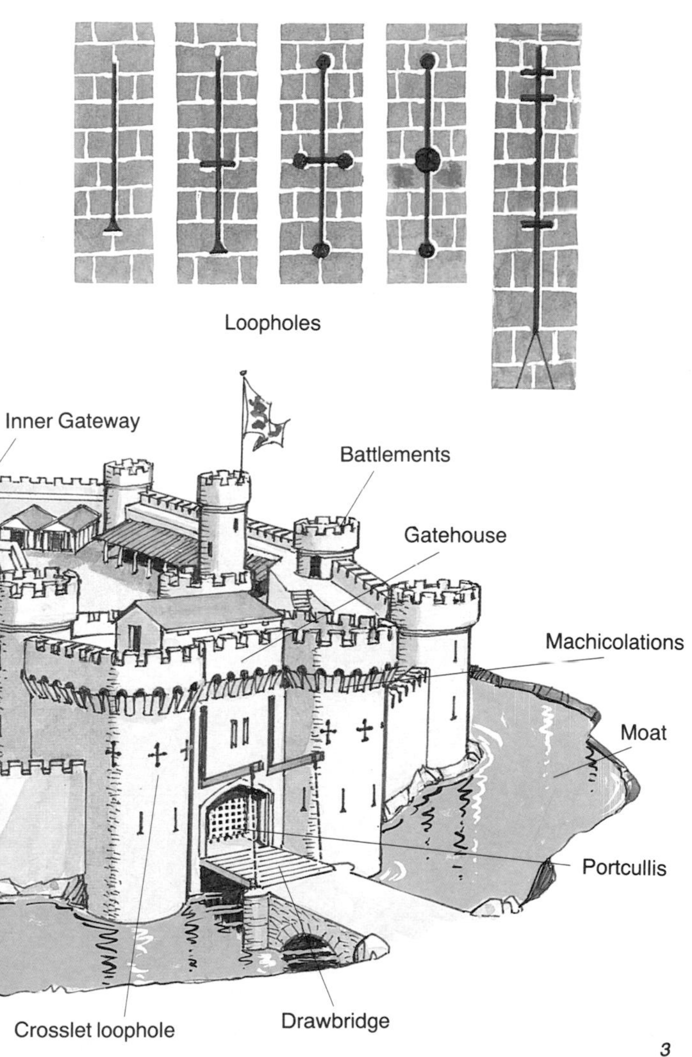
Loopholes
Inner Gateway
Battlements
Gatehouse
Machicolations
Moat
Portcullis
Crosslet loophole
Drawbridge

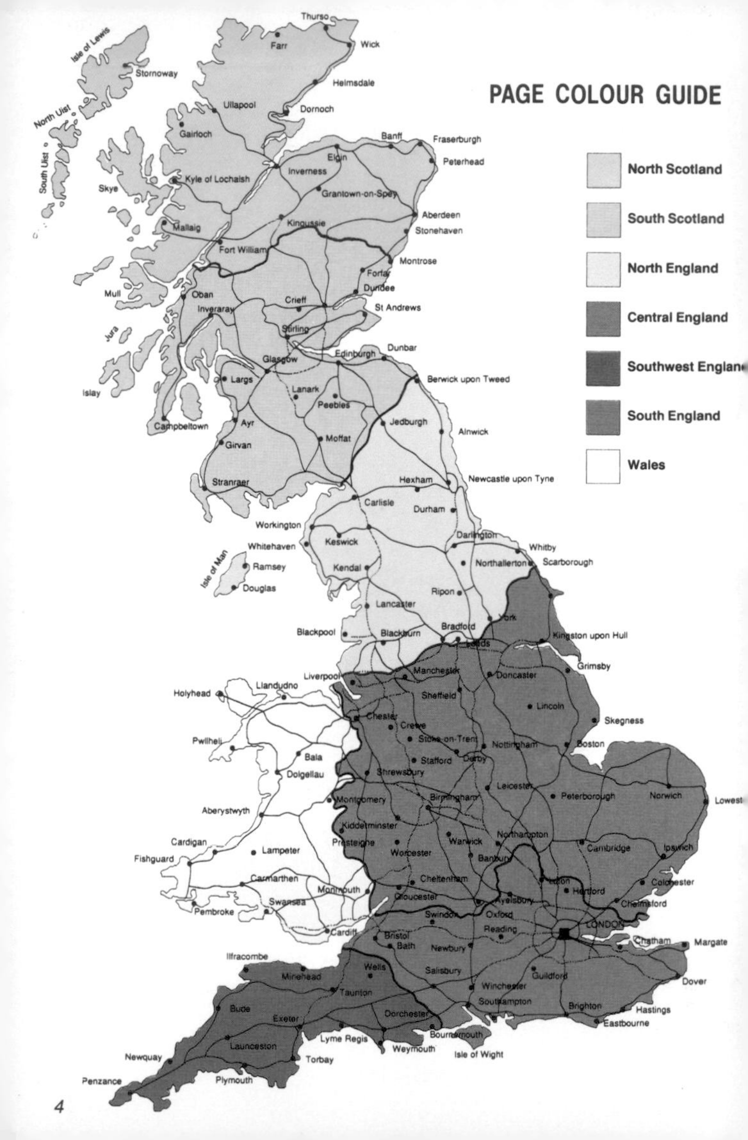
PAGE COLOUR GUIDE
North Scotland
South Scotland
North England
Central England
South England
Wales
Thurso
Farr
Wick
Isle of Lewis
Stornoway
Helmsdale
Ullapool
Dornoch
North Uist
Gairloch
South Uist
Banff
Fraserburgh
Peterhead
Elgin
Inverness
Skye
Kyle of Lochalsh
Grantown-on-Spey
Aberdeen
Stonehaven
Mallaig
Kingussie
Fort William
Montrose
Forfar
Dundee
Mull
Oban
Crieff
Inveraray
St Andrews
Jura
Stirling
Dunbar
Glasgow
Edinburgh
Largs
Berwick upon Tweed
Islay
Lanark
Peebles
Campbeltown
Ayr
Jedburgh
Alnwick
Girvan
Moffat
Stranraer
Hexham
Newcastle upon Tyne
Carlisle
Durham
Workington
Keswick
Darlington
Whitehaven
Whitby
Isle of Man
Ramsey
Northallerton
Scarborough
Kendal
Douglas
Ripon
Lancaster
York
Bradford
Blackpool
Blackburn
Kingston upon Hull
Leeds
Grimsby
Liverpool
Manchester
Doncaster
Holyhead
Llandudno
Sheffield
Lincoln
Chester
Skegness
Crewe
Pwllheli
Stoke-on-Trent
Nottingham
Boston
Bala
Stafford
Derby
Dolgellau
Shrewsbury
Leicester
Peterborough
Norwich
Montgomery
Birmingham
Aberystwyth
Kidderminster
Northampton
Cardigan
Presteigne
Warwick
Cambridge
Ipswich
Lampeter
Worcester
Fishguard
Banbury
Carmarthen
Cheltenham
Luton
Colchester
Monmouth
Hertford
Gloucester
Aylesbury
Chelmsford
Swansea
Pembroke
Swindon
Oxford
LONDON
Reading
Cardiff
Bristol
Chatham
Margate
Bath
Newbury
Ilfracombe
Wells
Salisbury
Guildford
Dover
Minehead
Winchester
Taunton
Southampton
Bude
Brighton
Hastings
Exeter
Dorchester
Eastbourne
Bournemouth
Lyme Regis
Launceston
Weymouth
Isle of Wight
Newquay
Torbay
Penzance
Plymouth

Egremont Castle; built of red sandstone in the 12th century.
*I-Spy for **20***

Lowther Castle is the home of the Earl of Lonsdale.
*I-Spy for **10***

Kendal Castle was the home of Catherine Parr. Who was she?
*I-Spy for **15***
Double with answer

Carlisle Castle was often laid siege to by the Scots.
*I-Spy for **10***

The keep of **Brougham Castle** is called the Pagan Tower.
*I-Spy for **15***

Muncaster Castle was rebuilt in the 1860s for Lord Muncaster.
*I-Spy for **15***

Wray Castle was built in 1847 by Dr James Dawson.
*I-Spy for **10***

Sizergh Castle has relics of Charles Edward Stuart. Who was he?
*I-Spy for **15***
Double with answer

Barnard Castle was named after its founder, Bernard de Balliol.
*I-Spy for **15***

Auckland Castle contains a splendid Gothic Throne Room
*I-Spy for **15***

Lord Neville received a licence to crenellate **Raby Castle**.
*I-Spy for **10***

Bowes Castle, built between 1176-1188, is an impressive ruin.
*I-Spy for **20***

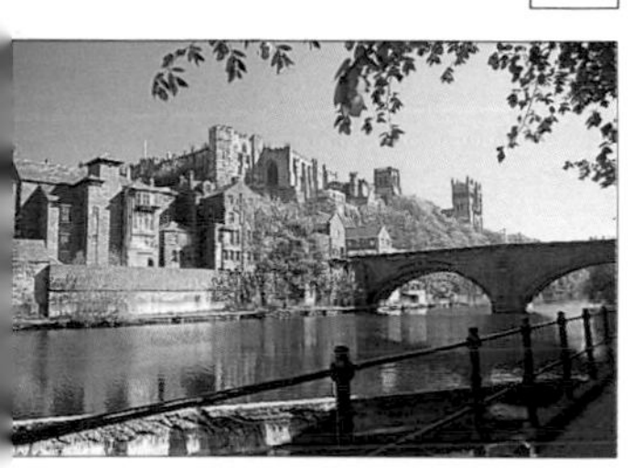

Durham Castle was donated to the University in the 19th century.
*I-Spy for **15***

Castle Clitheroe keep is the smallest known. True or false?
*I-Spy for **20***
Double with answer

Hornby Castle, built in the 14th century, was enlarged in the 19th.
*I-Spy for **20***

In **Warkworth Castle**, who did the Earl of Northumberland plot to kill?
*I-Spy for **10** Double with answer*

Bamburgh Castle was besieged by William II in the 11th century.
*I-Spy for **10***

Lindisfarne Castle was seized by Jacobite supporters in 1725.
*I-Spy for **15***

The proud ruins of **Dunstanburgh Castle** bear signs of many battles.
*I-Spy for **20***

Alnwick Castle belongs to the Duke of Northumberland.
*I-Spy for **15***

Mary Queen of Scots was a prisoner in **Bolton Castle** in 1568-9.
*I-Spy for **20***

Helmsley Castle was owned by the Dukes of Buckingham until 1689.
*I-Spy for **20***

Castle Howard was built by the third Earl of Carlisle in 1725.
*I-Spy for **15***

Pickering Castle was first built in wood, then rebuilt in stone in 1324.
*I-Spy for **15***

Knaresborough Castle was home to one of Thomas à Becket's assassins. What was his name?
*I-Spy for **15***
Double with answer

Edward IV gave **Middleham Castle** to his brother Richard III.
*I-Spy for **20***

Richmond Castle has England's olde
Great Hall. How old is it?
*I-Spy for **10***
Double with answer

The 12th century **Scarborough Castle** is built on the site of a Roman fort.
*I-Spy for **10***

Conisbrough Castle has unusual soli
towers with no rooms.
*I-Spy for **15***

Skipton Castle is still lived in, after 700 years of history.
*I-Spy for **20***

Beeston Castle was built in 1225 and ruined in 1646 after a siege by Roundheads. How?
*I-Spy for **15***
Double with answer

The new wing of **Bolsover Castle** was built as a luxurious home in 1613 on the site of an earlier fortress.
*I-Spy for **10***
Double with answer

Peveril Castle is named after William Peveril the bailiff who built it in 1080. What was a bailiff?
*I-Spy for **10***
Double with answer

Mow Cop is a fake castle built in 1754 by a land-owner who wanted a fine view. What is such a building called?
*I-Spy for **20***
Double with answer

Colchester Castle was built on the site of a Roman temple.
*I-Spy for **20***

Edward II was slain in **Berkeley Castle**. On whose orders?
*I-Spy for **20***
Double with answer

Sudeley Castle was restored in the 19th century.
*I-Spy for **15***

Hedingham Castle was owned by the Earls of Oxford from 1140 until 1713.
*I-Spy for **10***

Clearwell Castle was battlemented in the mid 18th century.
*I-Spy for **10***

Eastnor Castle was built in 1812 by Lord Somers.
*I-Spy for **10***

Croft Castle was rebuilt as a luxury home in the last century.
*I-Spy for **15***

Goodrich Castle guards a ford on the Wye River.
*I-Spy for **20***

Most of **Dudley Castle** was built in 1300. What is in the grounds?
*I-Spy for **20***
Double with answer

Hertford Castle dates back to Saxon times but is mostly 17th century.
*I-Spy for **10***

Belvoir Castle has been rebuilt five times, most recently in 1830.
*I-Spy for **10***

1700 houses were demolished to build **Lincoln Castle** in 1068.
*I-Spy for **10***

Bolingbroke Castle dates from 1200. Which English king was born here?
*I-Spy for **20***
Double with answer

Ashby de la Zouch Castle was defended by Royalists in a long siege 1644-46.
*I-Spy for **20***

Nearly 1 million bricks were used to build **Tattershall Castle** in 1436.
*I-Spy for **20***

Castle Acre, built on a Roman site, is linked to a large priory.
*I-Spy for **20***

Norwich Castle; for what purpose is the castle used today?
*I-Spy for **15***
Double with answer

Little remains of **Nottingham Castle** after a disastrous fire in 1831.
*I-Spy for **10***

Newark Castle was besieged three times during the Civil War.
*I-Spy for **10***

Rockingham Castle was converted into a comfortable house in 1530.
*I-Spy for **10***

Ludlow Castle, abandoned in 1651, was allowed to fall into ruin.
*I-Spy for **10***

Broughton Castle; named after John de Broughton who built it in 1301.
*I-Spy for **15***

Shrewsbury Castle was converted into a private home in 1730.
*I-Spy for **10***

Clun Castle is famous for its extensive earthworks and ditches.
*I-Spy for **20***

Hopton Castle was built near the Welsh Marches in the 12th century.
*I-Spy for **15***

Stokesay Castle is in fact a fortified manor house.
*I-Spy for **20***

Framlingham Castle's 12th century walls have often been captured.
*I-Spy for **15***

Warwick Castle has been continuously inhabited since it was built in 1068.
*I-Spy for **20***

Only the immense keep remains of **Orford Castle**, built in 1165.
*-Spy for **20***

Tutbury Castle was badly damaged during the Civil War.
*I-Spy for **10***

Tintagel Castle is the traditional birthplace of King Arthur.
*I-Spy for **20***

The odd circular castle of **Restormel**, has no towers or buttresses.
*I-Spy for **20***

Built in 1545, **Pendennis Castle** protected Falmouth Harbour.
*I-Spy for **20***

St Mawes was built to house artillery in 1540 by Henry VIII.
*I-Spy for **20***

Launceston Castle was ruined in the Civil War by Roundheads.
*I-Spy for **10***

Built in 1484, **Dartmouth Castle** was designed to carry cannon.
*I-Spy for **20***

Castle Drogo; built in 1910 by Julius Drewe on his ancestral lands.
*I-Spy for **20***

Powderham Castle has been altered many times in its 900 year history.
*I-Spy for **10***

Most of **Bickleigh Castle** is 16th century. Some is twice as old.
*I-Spy for **10***

Okehampton was abandoned in 1537 when its owner was executed.
*I-Spy for **10***

Old Sherborne Castle was destroyed in 1642 during the Civil War.
*I-Spy for **10***

The huge central mound of **Totnes Castle**, built in 1320.
*I-Spy for **20***

The shattered ruins of **Christchurch Castle** stand in a hotel garden.
*I-Spy for **10***

The vast ruins of **Corfe Castle**. Which English king was murdered here?
*I-Spy for **20***
Double with answer

New **Sherborne Castle** was built by Sir Walter Raleigh in 1594.
*I-Spy for **10***

The 12th century **Taunton Castle** stands on a pre-Roman site.
*I-Spy for **15***

Dunster Castle has been inhabited by the Luttrells since 1376.
*I-Spy for **15***

The beautiful little village castle of **Nunney**, built in 1373.
*I-Spy for **20***

The Tower of London has always belonged to the monarch.
*I-Spy for **15***

Traitor's Gate was the entrance used by prisoners arriving by boat.
*I-Spy for **5***

The Round Tower provides the main entrance to the castle.
*I-Spy for **10***

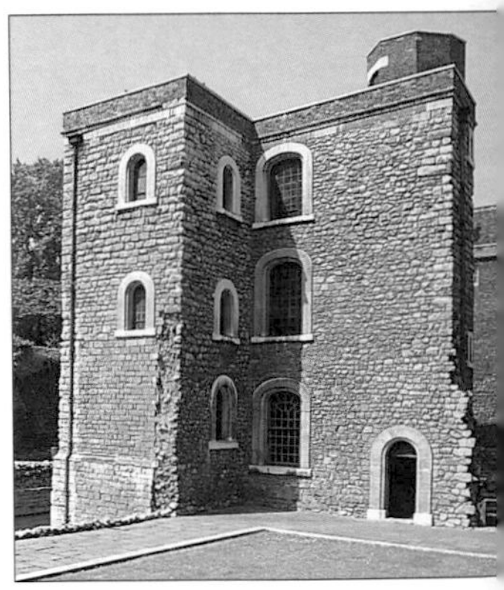

The Jewel Tower. It houses the Crown Jewels. True or false?
*I-Spy for **5***
Double with answer

The White Tower is the oldest section, dating back to the 11th century.
*I-Spy for **5***

The gatehouse is all that remains of **Donnington Castle**.
I-Spy for ***15***

The ramparts and towers of **Chiddingstone Castle** were added in the 19th century.
I-Spy for ***15***

Windsor Castle has been a royal residence for 900 years.
I-Spy for ***20***

Norman **Portchester Castle** is surrounded by Roman Walls.
I-Spy for ***20***

Canterbury Castle was built in about 1080, and abandoned around 1600.
I-Spy for ***10***

Hever Castle was restored by American millionaire W.W. Astor in 1903.
*I-Spy for **15***

Dover Castle is one of the largest and best preserved in England.
*I-Spy for **10***

Chilham Castle, a manor house buil in 1616 to replace the old castle.
*I-Spy for **10***

Leeds Castle has been called the most beautiful in England.
*I-Spy for **20***

Deal Castle; built in 1538 to deter a French invasion.
*I-Spy for **20***

ochester Castle has the tallest keep
Britain, built in 1127.
*Spy for **15***

Charming **Scotney Castle**
was built in about 1380.
*I-Spy for **20***

urstmonceaux Castle
as built in 1440 and
stored in 1913.
*Spy for **10***

uildford Castle was built in
)70 to protect a river
ossing.
*Spy for **10***

Bodiam Castle was built in 1385 and
has featured in many movies.
*I-Spy for **20***

Carisbrooke Castle. Who was imprisoned here in 1647?
*I-Spy for **20***
Double with answer

Arundel Castle was largely destroy[ed] in 1643 and rebuilt in 1791 and 1890.
*I-Spy for **20***

Lewes Castle is dominated by two 13th century towers.
*I-Spy for **15***

Pevensey Castle was refortified in 1940 to repel a possible German invasion.
*I-Spy for **20***

Rye Castle is all that remains of t[he] extensive town walls.
*I-Spy for **10***

Balmoral Castle is the Royal Family's holiday home. Who bought it in 1852?

*I-Spy for **10***
Double with answer

Braemar Castle was a garrison for Hanoverian troops in 1786.
*I-Spy for **15***

Craigievar Castle has corbelled towers and conical roofs.
*I-Spy for **10***

The Marquis of Montrose had **Brodie Castle** burned in 1635.
*I-Spy for **20***

Castle Fraser was built by the families of Bel and Leiper.
*I-Spy for **15***

Kildrummy Castle was created by St Gilbert, last Scottish saint.
*I-Spy for **10***

Kisimul Castle's owners were pirates in the 17th century.
*I-Spy for **20***

Breacachadh Castle is home for the Macleans of Coll
*I-Spy for **15***

The **Crathes Castle** treasure is a horn of fluted ivory.
*I-Spy for **15***

What famous treasure was smuggled out of **Dunnottar Castle** in 1652?
*I-Spy for **20***
Double with answer

Ardvreck Castle was built by the Macleods of Assynt.
*I-Spy for **20***

Duart Castle was lost to Hector Maclean in 1745 for supporting Bonnie Prince Charlie.
*I-Spy for **15***

Castle Tiorum was burnt by its owner, Chief of the Macdonalds of Clan Ranald, in 1715.
*I-Spy for **15***

Castle Moil was a defence against raiding Norsemen.
*I-Spy for **15***

Cawdor Castle appears in which of Shakespeare's plays?
*I-Spy for **10***
Double with answer

Dating back to 1220, the castle of **Eilean Donan** is on an islet of Loch Duich and connected by a causeway. It was a garrison for Spanish Jacobite troops in 1719 when the castle, now restored, was blown up by an English man o'war.
*I-Spy for **15***

Dunrobin Castle is the seat of which Earls and Dukes?
*I-Spy for **15***
Double with answer

Dunvegan Castle: home of the MacLeods of MaeLeod.
*I-Spy for **20***

Duntulm Castle was the seat of the Macdonalds of Sleat.
*I-Spy for **15***

rquhart Castle was blown up in 392 to prevent it being occupied / Jacobite rebels.
*Spy for **15***

The two castles **Girnigoe** and **Sinclair** are cliff-edge ruins.
*I-Spy for **20***

ictorian **Inverness Castle** is ow a Sheriff Court and jail.
*Spy for **10***

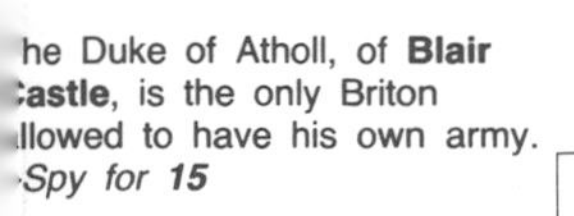

he Duke of Atholl, of **Blair astle**, is the only Briton llowed to have his own army.
*Spy for **15***

Wrought-iron grilles protect the windows of **Elcho Castle**.
I-Spy for ***10***

Edzell Castle, mostly a ruin, has a 16th century tower house.
I-Spy for ***10***

Glamis Castle was the childhood home of Her Majesty the Queen Mother.
I-Spy for ***15***

Invermark Castle, owned by the Stirling family, is now a ruin.
I-Spy for ***15***

It was to **Hermitage Castle** that Mary Queen of Scots galloped to visit her lover, Lord Bothwell.
*I-Spy for **15***

Thirlestane Castle, built of pink sandstone, has many turrets and fine 17th century ceilings.
*I-Spy for **10***

Medieval **Neidpath Castle** has a rock-hewn well, a pit prison and walls nearly 12 feet thick.
*I-Spy for **20***

Floors Castle, built in the 18th century, was the location for the Tarzan film 'Greystoke'.
*I-Spy for **10***

Castle Campbell, was burned by Oliver Cromwell's men in the 17th century.
*I-Spy for **15***

Cardoness Castle was the 15th to 16th century home of the McCullochs of Galloway. It has a vaulted basement.
*I-Spy for **20***

In 1330 Edward I laid siege to **Caerlaverock Castle**. Over its gate are heavy machicolations.
*I-Spy for **15***

Stirling Castle was captured and recaptured many times. Who was born in the castle in 1430?
*I-Spy for **10***
Double with answer

unskey Castle, on a headland oint, is an impressive ruin.
-Spy for **20**

Aberdour Castle was built in the 14th century. When did the Douglas family abandon it?
*I-Spy for **15***
Double with answer

he castle of **Drumlanrig** as Renaissance towers, alustrades and many windows.
*-Spy for **10***

Surrendered to James II in 1455, **Threave Castle** was a stronghold of the Black Douglasses.
*I-Spy for **15***

Edward I laid siege to **Dirleton Castle** in 1298. Now in ruins the castle dates back to 1225.
*I-Spy for **10***

Kellie Castle, owned by the Earls of Mar and Kellie, was restored 100 years ago.
*I-Spy for **10***

Grim and forbidding, fortified **Blackness Castle** was once used as
a prison.
*I-Spy for **15***

The notorious Cardinal Beaton was murdered in 1546 at
St Andrews Castle.
*I-Spy for **15***

Mary, Queen of Scots and Lord Bothwell found sanctuary at **Hailes Castle** in 1567.
*I-Spy for **15***

Luffness Castle was enlarged in the 16th century, but its keep is 13th century.
*I-Spy for **15***

Lauriston Castle was begun in the 16th century. On its north side is a very small watch chamber.
*I-Spy for **10***

Edinburgh Castle is steeped in history. Its earliest part is the 12th century St Margaret's Chapel. King James VI (I of England) was born there. The castle has been a fortress, a treasury, a refuge for sovereigns and a prison.
*I-Spy for **10***

In **Culzean Castle** is a flat given to President Eisenhower.
*I-Spy for **10***

The spectacular ruins of **Bothwell Castle**, once the largest stone castle in Scotland.
*I-Spy for **10***

Dumbarton Castle was taken from Lord Fleming by escalade in 1568.
*I-Spy for **15***

Brodick Castle, parts of which are 13th century, belongs to the Dukes of Hamilton.
*I-Spy for **15***

Barcaldine Castle, one of many owned by the Campbells, fell into ruin and was later restored.
*I-Spy for **15***

Vhen was **Rothesay Castle** stormed
ınd breached by Norsemen?
*·Spy for **10***
)ouble with answer

Glen App Castle, built in the 1890s, was a hospital in World War II.
*I-Spy for **15***

<ilchurn **Castle** was taken by
ꟷlanoverian troops in 1746.
*·Spy for **10***

Victorian **Torosay Castle** is built in Scottish Baronial style.
*I-Spy for **15***

Inveraray Castle was begun in 1743 and has been the seat of the Dukes of Argyll for centuries.
*I-Spy for **15***

Chirk Castle is owned by the Myddleton family whose ancestor bought it in 1595.
*I-Spy for **10***

Denbigh Castle was built during the reign of Edward I. What was Edward I's nickname?
*I-Spy for **20***
Double with answer

Ewloe Castle was strengthened in 1257 by Prince Llewelyn ap Gruffydd of Wales.
*I-Spy for **15***

Rhuddlan Castle was built in the reign of Edward I, as a fortress.
*I-Spy for **10***

Ruthin Castle was built in the 13th century, ruined in the Civil War and is now a hotel.
I-Spy for ***15***

Carew Castle belonged to Rys ap Thomas when he fought for Henry Tudor in 1485. Against whom?
I-Spy for ***15***
Double with answer

Edward I's fort, **Aberystwyth Castle**, was taken by the Welsh under Owain Glyndwr in 1404.
I-Spy for ***10***

In 1426, in the Wars of the Roses, **Carreg Cennen Castle** was the scene of bitter fighting.
I-Spy for ***15***

Kidwelly Castle, has a splendid 14th century gatehouse.
*I-Spy for **5***

Manorbier Castle was first built in the reign of Henry I. Who was his father?
*I-Spy for **10***
Double with answer

The magnificent keep of **Pembroke Castle,** built by William Marshall, Earl of Pembroke in 1200.
*I-Spy for **10***

Tenby Castle was razed to the ground in 1150, rebuilt and later besieged by Oliver Cromwell.
*I-Spy for **15***

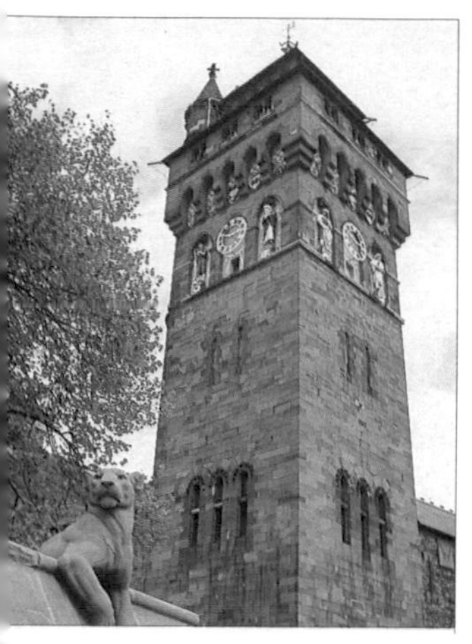

Cardiff Castle was begun during the reign of King William II. Why was he known as Rufus?
*I-Spy for **10***
Double with answer

Abergavenny Castle was taken from King John's forces by Prince Llewelyn of Wales in 1215.
*I-Spy for **15***

Caudicote Castle has machicolations through which molten lead was poured on attackers.
*I-Spy for **5***

Chepstow Castle was begun just one year after the Battle of Hastings. What was the date?
*I-Spy for **15***
Double with answer

Monmouth Castle is famous for being the birthplace of Henry V. What was his greatest battle?
*I-Spy for **10***
Double with answer

Raglan Castle was started in about 1435. Its great keep is known as the Yellow Tower of Gwent.
*I-Spy for **20***

Skenfrith Castle was given by King John to Hubert de Burgh. What was John's nickname?
*I-Spy for **15***
Double with answer

ʜubert de Burgh, owner of the **White Castle**, urged King John to sign which charter in 1215?
*I-Spy for **15***
Double with answer

Beaumaris Castle took 35 years to build. Before it was finished it had already begun to disintegrate.
*I-Spy for **20***

Caernarfon Castle was built in 1283 by Edward I, after he had captured the northern castles of Wales.
*I-Spy for **10***

Conwy Castle, built in 1288, was sold in 1628 to Viscount Conway for only £100. Why?
*I-Spy for **10***
Double with answer

Dolwyddelan Castle was built in 1170 in the reign of King Henry II. Was he a Norman king?
*I-Spy for **20***
Double with answer

Criccieth Castle is now a ruin. It was burned down in 1400 by the Welsh hero Owain Glyndwr.
*I-Spy for **15***

Gwydyr Castle was built in Tudor times. It has a beautiful chapel, with a splendid painted ceiling.
*I-Spy for **25***

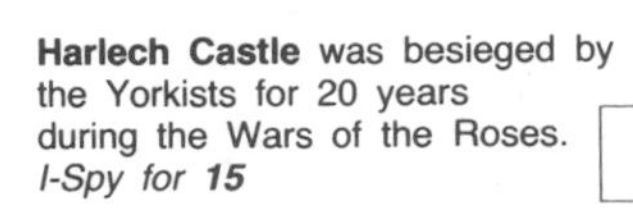

Harlech Castle was besieged by the Yorkists for 20 years during the Wars of the Roses.
*I-Spy for **15***

INDEX

D & G = Dumfries & Galloway
H & W = Hereford and Worcester
N'thum = Northumberland

ANSWERS

The 6th and last wife of Henry VIII p5
Bonnie Prince Charlie p6
True p7
Henry VI p8
Sir Hugh de Morville p9
900 years old p10
By demolishing the main defensive wall p11
A folly p11
An official who looked after a castle for the king p11
Roger Mortimer, the Earl of March p12
A zoo p13
Henry IV, known as Henry Bolingbroke p14
A town museum p15
King Edward the Martyr in 978 p20
False p22
King Charles I p26
Prince Albert, husband of Queen Victoria p27
Scottish regalia p28
Macbeth p29
Of Sutherland p30
The Scottish king James II p34
In 1700 p35
1240 p39
Longshanks p40
Richard III. Henry Tudor was Henry VII p41
William the Conqueror p42
Because he had red hair and a florid complexion. Rufus means red p43
1067 p44
Agincourt p44
Lackland p44
Magna Carta p45
Because it had fallen into decay p45
No. Angevin p46

ISBN 1 85671 114 5

A CIP record for this title is available from the British Library.

Written and edited by Martspress Ltd, Design Denis Gray.

The Publisher gratefully acknowledges the contribution of the Automobile Association who provided the majority of the photographs in this I-Spy book. Additional material was provided by Philip Craven and Rockingham Castle Estate Office. The Editor also thanks the Bedale, Dundee and Inverness Tourist Offices for their assistance.

Every care has been taken in the preparation of this I-Spy book to ensure that the factual information was correct at the time of going to press. Neither the publisher nor Editor accept any responsibility whatsoever for any loss, damage, injury, or inconvenience sustained or caused as a result of using this I-Spy book.

Colour reproduction by Norwich Litho Services Limited.

Printed in Spain.